Happy birthday!

John Wadding...

WILD TALES

FROM THE WEST

by

John Waddington-Feather

Published by Feather Books
PO Box 438
Shrewsbury SY3 0WN, UK
Tele/fax; 01743 872177

Website URL: http://www.waddysweb.freeuk.com
e-mail: john@waddysweb.freeuk.com

2001

Re-printed 2001

ISBN: 0 947718 82 6

No. 57 in the Feather Books Poetry Series

FOREWORD

Somewhere along the line, I suspect one of the
Waddington-Feather genes is that of a roaming Viking
invader from his native Yorkshire. For John's Muse is
never still. A poet of many moods and matching styles, he
reflects so much of his own up-bringing: a familiarity with
medieval literary tradition from his university days,
steeped withal in a longer tradition of Yorkshire dialect,
narrative verse from Old Norse and Old English sagas -
and finally an unwavering love of North American lore
and people.

So, he adopts the laid-back folksy style of the veteran
raconteur yarning from that 'throne of human felicity', the
tavern-chair, about death and dubious folk-heroes of
earlier days out West and North. He is at once witty,
subtly sardonic, occasionally satirical. His humour is racy
as 'a hot-rodding railroad'. And like so much good
poetry, his is best read aloud - preferably to a receptive
audience.

Prof. Eddie Edmonds
(Former Dean of Education, P.E.I. University, Canada.

PROFILE

The Revd John Waddington-Feather is an Anglican priest,
educationist and writer. He was born in Yorkshire,
England, and graduated in English Language and
Medieval Literature at Leeds University in 1954. His
published works include novels, drama, academic papers
and poetry which has appeared in several anthologies.
Much of his ministry and teaching has been in schools and
prisons.

iii

CONTENTS

JOE AND THE TALKING DOG

"49" Joe once told us a tale
which kept him in whisky a week;
concerning a barman he took for a ride
by selling a dog that could speak.

Dawson was where he sold him the pass
in a bar that's no more, glad to say;
for the bar-owner cheated the gold-miners bad
when they checked in their gold-dust for pay.

"Shaky Hand" Pete was that crooked guy's name,
'cos he shook like a leaf when he told
out the sourdough's dust that they paid him for booze
after months in the bush panning gold.

He'd cheated old Joe pretty mean once or twice
when he'd gone there to cash in his dust;
and for months Joe'd been thinking how he'd make it quits
and win back the dollars he'd lost.

It came to him sudden one night in a show
where he'd gone to a music-hall turn;
a ventriloquist throwing his voice from a doll,
a trick Joey vowed he would learn.

He paid the guy handsome to teach him his trade,
and Joe learned his lessons so well
he could throw out his voice from any darned place,
could ha'e thrown it from heaven to hell!

When he'd gotten smart at the voice-throwing trick,
he went out and bought him a dog;
a cross-eyed blue mongrel, as loonie as Len,
which grinned ear to ear like a hog.

He took him along to "Shaky Hand" Pete's
and asked for a plate full of stew;
then he ordered a drink - and as Pete passed them by
the dog hollered: "Please make that two!"

Pete's ears near dropped clean off of his head;
he stopped in his tracks like a log,
and stared all around before saying to Joe:
"Was it you who spoke then - or your dog?"

"'Twas me," croaked the dog. "I asked for a drink,
most civil, like all dogs well bred."
Pete near dropped the glasses he held in his hand
as his eyes popped out from his head.

But Joe went on eating like nothing was wrong
as his mongrel kept jawing away:
"Please don't stand there staring. It's rude, my good man.
Just bring me my drink and I'll pay."

"Say, Joe," said the barman, who spoke kinda slow,
"This crittur is yours, I believe?"
Joe threw him a glance and said: "Sure, that dog's mine."
Then wiped his mouth clean on his sleeve.

The barman laid out two full glasses of beer,
one by the dog, one by Joe,
before he shot off to tell to his wife
the way to make plenty of dough.

For she was the boss of that sleazy saloon;
she was greedy and mean, she was near.
She figured how they'd make their fortunes at once
with a dog that could talk and drink beer.

As soon as he'd gone, Joey drank the dog's beer,
it went down in one, cool and neat;
he swallowed that pint without spilling one drop,
then put the glass back at his feet.

Pete and his missus came in on the trot,
they'd been jawing some fast talk outside,
and were firmly agreed if Joe'd sell them his dog,
they could take the whole world in their stride.

"With that hound in our bar, we'd pull in more folks
than Tombstone and Prescott combined.
You'd have to spill gold-dust for over a year
what he'd earn in one night," she opined.

They walked in together and stared at the dog
with its empty beer glass standing near.
"Your dog is sure thirsty," the barman observed.
Said the mongrel: "It's mighty fine beer!"

Pete and his missus stared in surprise,
but she asked it a question or two;
to which that old hound-dog made such slick replies
she gave it a free plate of stew.

"You're kind," said the crittur, "but not too much salt
for it tends to give old dogs a thirst.
It's a helluva way to "'49's" stake
and I'd have to keep stoppin' - or burst!"

That did it! She offered Joe five hundred bucks,
but he said no way could he part
with a hound he could talk to out in the wild
and had grown very close to his heart.

Yet he said he owed dollars for grub down at Mac's,
where he'd whiskies chalked up by the score;
"If only you'd double your offer..." Joe said.
She snapped: "Done - but not half a cent more!"

At this the poor mongrel howled out aloud
and wailed: "Joe, what kinda friend's that,
who'll sell out his pardner for one thousand bucks
at less than the drop of a hat?"

"Sorry," said Joe, "but you see I'm flat broke;
I owe money all over the town -
and a good friend is one who'll help a guy out
when his luck's running low and way down."

"OK," whined the hound, "if you've made up your mind
on what you've decided to do..."
"I'm sorry," said Joe, "but you see how it is;
I've no choice but to let them buy you."

"If that is the case then," the mongrel replied,
as it watched Joey pocket the bid,
"I swear that I'll never again speak a word."
- and you know, that old dog never did!

THE ALBUQUERQUE BULLS-EYE

Way out West when all was virgin new,
when land was plenty and the folk were few;
when mules and oxen hauled the wagon-trains,
as pioneers streamed out across the plains;
homesteaders staked their claims by fits and starts
to break the sod which often broke their hearts.
The West was wild then, only for the brave,
you found your fortune, or you dug your grave.
But, oh, what land! So beautiful though wild,
it drew folk to it like a homesick child;
and still it draws with all its haunting power,
its mountains and its canyons, its wilderness in flower,
its rivers and its painted desert plains,
with startling skies the blood-red sunset stains.
But to my tale about one Billy Thacker,
renowned throughout the West a mighty whacker;
a wagon-driver expert with the whip,
so skilled, they claimed that Billy T. could strip
the sheets from off a bed without a peep,
and leave the lady in it fast asleep -
but I won't tell of Billy's early life,
he settled down and found himself a wife;
and wives can make the wildest fellows tame
when once they marry them and take their name.
That state of bliss befell young Billy Thacker;
he married a most winsome wench, a cracker,
the best in Albuquerque on the trail
to Santa Fe, the setting for this tale.
For there he met a cattle-king, so big
he filled the entire seat upon his gig;
no one could cope with his enormous bulk,
in girth and height he was a heaving hulk.
His big mouth also matched his massive frame

for bragging and for betting he acquired a name:
'Big-mouth' Buckster he was known afar,
from Santa Fe right up to Wichita.
He ranched some place, they said, near Midwest City,
and paid his cow-hands poor, which was a pity;
they'd run his steer to freight at Santa Fe,
then scarcely have the grub to make their way
back home along the trail east to the range,
where 'Big-mouth' always sold 'em short on change.
No wrangler worked for him till he grew old,
and Buckster hired rustlers, so I'm told;
he was the kinda guy who wheeled and botched,
a crook you kept an eye upon and watched.
A bar-man once bet Billy T. a dollar,
from twenty feet he couldn't remove his collar,
neat and tidy with his driver's whip.
Bill took it stud and all in one sweet flip,
clean as a card-trick off the bar-man's neck,
without a mark, without a single fleck.
Now 'Big-mouth' Buckster, who'd been on the bottle,
his face as red as crowing cockerel's wattle,
lost a packet on the driver's trick
taking off the collar with one flick.
"Bet you ten bucks you couldn't lift a dime
off the wagon here!" they heard him chime.
The wagon that he leaned on was a dray,
and Billy stood near forty feet away;
he eyed it slowly, said he'd need an hour
to make a longer whip an' try its power.
He'd take the bet, but Buckster had to bend
and place the dime upon his huge butt-end.
The cattle-king turned pale, but told the fellow
he'd use his butt to show he wasn't yellow;
so both agreed and marked the forty pitch

where Bill would try the ranchman's dime t'unhitch.
But in the hour before they had to meet
Bill wagered he'd make Buckster jump six feet;
and all unknown to 'Big-mouth' in the bar
the town outside laid bets from near and far,
wagering like mad down every street
Bill wouldn't make big Buckster jump six feet.
The hour ticked by, the two took up their stance,
the whole town came to watch the cattle-baron dance.
He did! He leapt a good six feet and more.
They heard in Texas 'Big-mouth' Buckster's roar,
as Billy Thacker's whip uncurled on high,
before it caught big Buckster's nether eye.
He missed the dime six inches, I declare,
but pinged old 'Big-mouth's' panic-button square.
They had to poultice him a week or more,
and even then it left him feeling sore;
he lost much weight, no longer standing big,
and always used a cushion in his gig.
The rancher never went to town again,
and for his butt - it's time to say "Amen".

THE BANK BUSTER

A proud and foolish folk in days of old
once tried to build a tower, so we're told;
an edifice which reached right to the sky,
where they could play at being gods on high.
More recently, sheer greed became the spur,
which sadly prompted one bright guy to err;
and build his golden tower slick and neat,
before it came down tumbling at his feet.
I knew him first as Wilmur Mammon Bland,
who built his airy tower upon sand -
or rather on derivatives and shares,
glossy, empty, unsubstantial wares.
Commodities that suited Wilmur well,
and helped him raise his golden tower pell-mell.
But once it crashed - it's usual in his game -
the cunning fellow went and changed his name.
He never shone at school, he was no scholar,
but yet he'd figure out an easy dollar
quicker than his teachers and their skills;
they worked at lessons, he at dollar bills.
He had another asset, too - his mouth,
with which he earned him money like the south
wind coaxing little apples onto trees;
he knew just how to flatter and to please.
Full fast he rose from office-boy to clerk;
his bosses recognised he was no jerk,
and soon promoted him within the bank
he'd joined, and that indeed became the plank
to golden hoards beyond his wildest dreams;
in next to no time he'd imagined schemes
to make himself a million bucks, his first -
but not his last. You see he had a thirst,
unquenchable it seemed, a crazy need

to satisfy an all-consuming greed.
Was he the only one who worshipped wealth?
Oh, no! The bank's directors with more stealth
worked hand-in-glove with Bland to fill their coffers;
they gave a him a carte blanche to make the offers
for derivatives throughout the world.
And how their wild young agent flung and hurled
the bank's reserves at every likely chance.
He led the auditors a merry dance!
All done legally, or so they said;
he never lost a wink of sleep in bed,
never once considered he might stumble;
he wasn't one for ever being humble.
And so young Wilmur's tower grew higher and higher,
and just when he considered he'd aspire
to join his bosses and their piles of cash,
the market in derivatives went crash.
So did the bank! Cleaned out of every cent,
reserves, life-saving, pensions, all were spent;
and all done legally, of course, though gambling.
The laughing lawyers made a kill unscrambling
the legal tangles Wilmur left behind;
such the sorry way fate deals the blind.
The bank's investors every one went plunk,
and Wilmur and his bosses did a bunk;
bolting to foreign havens safe abroad,
where once they'd had the foresight to unload
the profits from their palmy golden days.
When bankers gamble, the investor pays.
And safe abroad Bland changed his name to Bolovics,
to make himself a mint in Russian politics!

THE PIG REPORTER

An editor called Ivader T. Squeake
once had a dream that haunted him a week;
a nightmare which put paid to his repose
and centred on his journalistic nose.
As Squeake had no ideals or aspirations,
his tabloid shattered many reputations.
For principled reporting he'd no truck,
his paper thrived on social slime and muck.
As vultures home upon a rotting carcass.
so Ivader made rotten deeds his focus.
To catch a dirty scoop he poked and pried
in folks' privacy, and often lied.
Down deep he'd dig in personal affairs,
then claim that what he found was his, not theirs.
"I have right," he'd bleat, "to print my views
on anything as long as it sells news."
But truth in what he wrote was rarely there,
although he always swore he laid it bare.
The truth was that he never really knew it;
he'd swallow any gossip then he'd spew it
out in headlines, kill the truth stone-dead.
Not once did consequences fill his head;
still less make any impact on his heart.
When wrong he'd whine: "I only played my part
in trying to uncover vital facts,
the way that any good reporter acts."
His writing flowed from many poisonous pens,
backed up by a prying camera lens.
Princes, presidents, potentates - the lot,
a hint of scandal, Squeake was on the spot.
Film-stars, financiers, freaks - you name 'em,
Ivader T. Squeake was there to frame 'em.
His nose worked best on muddiest ground,

and when he'd picked up dirty smells he'd hound
his victims till he got a story.
It brought them shame but covered him with glory.
As you'd expect and probably you've guessed,
he was promoted to chief editor's desk.
And there he had a field-day sealing fates
of famous people right across the States.
His reputation soared as each edition
sent a leading figure to perdition.
His motto was: "We print to sell!"
He didn't give a damn whose life was hell.
Until that night he had this frightful dream
which changed his life and pricked his self-esteem.
His nose had smelled a most salacious story,
full of sex and violence most gory.
The guy was always guided by his nose,
and in his dream determined to expose
the sordid situation. It dragged him out
hot upon the trail, that dirty snout,
wading through the filthiest slime and mire,
familiar paths, which never led him higher.
When suddenly an awful change took place
about his nether regions and his face.
He felt his nose which now had grown quite big,
then realised he'd turned into a pig!
He howled and wailed and screamed aloud,
till soon about him pressed a crowd.
He stood, a little hog filled full of shame,
who'd dragged through all the mire his own good name.
At first, the press believed it some daft stunt,
until he opened wide his mouth to grunt:
"It's me! Ivader T. Squeake, I say!
Stop pestering me! Push off and go away!"
But no, they clung the closer like a leech,

15

never let the poor guy out of reach.
And next day's papers ran the stark headline:
"THE TRUTH REVEALED! SQUEAKE REALLY IS A SWINE!"
To end his dream he saw his cherished chair
filled by another pig sat grunting there.
And at that point he woke in consternation,
quickly handing in his resignation.
Henceforth he shunned all scandal, living meekly,
and wrote the pig page for a farmers' weekly.

THE FLAGSTAFF FLYER

Arizona State boasts many bards,
whose tales are wilder than their own backyards;
and they were pretty wild in days of old,
if I believe one half of what I'm told.
These south-western bards have tongues like butter,
to tell the far-fetched tales they sometimes utter.
One quoted me a story pin-brand new,
and swore on oath that all he said was true.
It was about a guy who lived at Flagstaff,
known far and wide as Obadiah Wagstaff.
Ob Wagstaff claimed he came from gentle stock,
an aristocrat as chimey as a clock.
He wore an eye-glass, spoke refined and suave,
and when at table never deigned to carve.
His voice was sweet, he had a practised grin,
used frequently to pull the ladies in.
Others, too, he pulled to sell his wares.
And, oh, he gave himself such genteel airs!
He made his living selling patent cures
which fixed just everything from colds to snores -
or so he said. His mixture fixed bad hearts
and shifted flatulence and chronic farts.
Especially it eased trapped wind, cured all;
so good, he never had to shout or bawl
to sell his famous patent panacea;
to buy it folks rode in from far and near.
He sold entirely by golden prattle -
then took their cash. He loved to hear it rattle!
He hired the best hotel. No high-street hack
who lived in lodgings like a common quack.
Behind his name he'd letters by the score,
from sev'ral universities. He swore
he'd been to Yale and Harvard in his youth,
more latterly at Phoenix where, forsooth,
degrees are earned by time and effort spent,
not given away with tokens, ten a cent.

So Obadiah made himself a name,
from Flagstaff to Grand Canyon basked in fame.
Until that fatal day he fell from grace
and fled the State of Arizona in disgrace.
When I say 'fled' I mean indeed he flew,
fired two hundred miles straight from a loo,
a thunderbox which overhung a stream,
propelled there all the way by his own steam.
It happened thus: the Mayor of Flagstaff grumbled
that Ob's patent wonder drug had rumbled
round his aching gut the livelong day
producing wind, not easing it, he had to say.
Once **he** spoke out then others followed quick;
they'd drunk his cure for weeks but still felt sick.
The game was up, and wily Wagstaff fled
one night while all were fast asleep in bed.
He'd promised that he'd pay their money back,
but packed his bags and fled, the rotten quack!
Disguised he left before he caught a larrup,
and hurried east to board the train at Gallup
and start again his tricks at Santa Fe.
He never made it there, I'm glad to say.
En route he tried to con the gentle Hopi,
booking in to sell his wares at Walpi,
unaware his reputation ran before him
and at the village they were ready for him.
He gave them all his smooth talk fine and fair,
as they congregated in the square.
Polite, the silent Hopis heard him out,
but watched him keenly as he spread about
his bottles filled with useless coloured brew,
shiny bright and nicely labelled, too.
Now the canny Hopis on their reservation
cured their stock of chronic constipation,
by giving them a drench that packed a kick
to unblock mulish bowels double-quick.
Unknown to Obadiah they switched his brew

with their own age-old drench before he knew,
and said they'd buy his cure if he drank first.
"Of course," said Obadiah, who'd got a thirst,
and drank the drenchy bottle dry pell-mell.
What followed next I scarcely dare to tell!
Poor Wagstaff felt a fire burn out his belly;
his face went white, then red, his legs turned jelly;
his gut began to swell like a balloon;
he tried to puke, but fell down in a swoon.
When he revived, he sought the nearest john
which he sprinted to and sat upon.
The one most handy overhung a drop,
at least three hundred feet from base to top.
For centuries the hut had housed the needy,
and that day Obadiah slid in speedy,
farting loudly like a thunderclap.
He was near blinded by the blast, poor chap!
Those standing near it glimpsed a nether hell,
were nearly smothered by the evil smell,
when that old john was blown to smithereens
by blasts that might have come from tons of beans,
released like claps of thunder from his bum
before he blew himself to Kingdom Come -
or so they thought - for out of sight Ob flew
just like a rocket. For months they never knew
where Obadiah Wagstaff came to earth.
All Arizona was convulsed with mirth.
In time, they heard he'd landed up in Utah,
where folks are clever, somewhat cuter,
and Obadiah never tried his tricks again,
but settled down to work in Hurricane.
Where all his life he lived a man apart,
famed far and wide as Flagstaff's biggest fart.

THE BUREAUCRATIC ASS

From Washington they sent a federal guy,
a bureaucrat in office very high,
way out West to look into the state's affairs
on conservation. He was full of airs,
city-slick though with a low profile,
for he was shifty, ramjam full of guile.
A bureaucrat, office-born and bred,
laws and regulations filled his head.
He'd left his college with a good degree,
a lawyer full of weighty law was he.
But often is the law a braying ass,
and so indeed for him it came to pass.
When senate ratified a clause that stopped
a rancher taking out a lion that copped
his cattle; or a bear that ate his meat,
then did this lawyer roll up fast and neat
to book law-breakers quickly on the spot.
Nor could a logger fell his little lot
if it was proved the Ten-toed Owl lived there,
or if the Greater-crested Craphawk chanced to dare
the leafy haunts in search of mate.
He stopped all logging; that was his pet hate.
Now, conservation has its part to play,
for if the greedy always had their way
our land would be a desert through and through,
and all the people in it stark yahoo.
To husband what God gave us is our lot;
not to grab and brag how much we've got.
The land belongs to all of us, that's just;
and those who ranch or farm it hold in trust
for all of us our nation's Godly soil.
It isn't ours to plunder or despoil,
still less to slaughter or eradicate

that which bounteous nature did create.
Reason God gave Man to work His ends;
but reason all the time flawed Mankind bends.
He twists it every way for gain or power;
for selfish ends he turns sweet reason sour.
The federal guy was very full of self,
puffed up with pride and other worthless pelf.
A politician readymade, it seemed,
but to the top another way he'd schemed.
He was the Inspector General of State,
empowered to oversee and regulate
each natural habitat, each farm, each ranch,
each stack of timber to the smallest branch.
Someone told him that down Prescott way,
the cowboys there...a mere rumor of hearsay...
and rumors have a way of gathering strength
when they're passed around for any length.
Chameleon-like they seem to take on colour
to suit both hearers' ears and flim-flam teller...
but as I said, the cowboys there, if rumor
is to be at all believed...and humor,
too, has part to play in what's now said,
and may the good Lord strike me dead
if I add but a single stroke of colour
to the tale that I was told. A fuller
couldn't whiten whiter what I say,
this bar-room story told down Prescott way...
but as I said, upon a rumor hung
this tale by which the Inspector guy was stung,
stung by a drunken burro that could talk,
who met the snooping Wally on a walk,
as he sneaked by the roadside from his car.
In truth, he hadn't wandered very far,
but stopped dead in his tracks when with a bray

21

the talking donkey called and made him stay.
"Good sir," he said, " if you've a moment free,
please stop and pass the time of day with me."
The snooper couldn't scarce believe his ears!
"Who spoke?" he cried. The donkey topped two beers -
he had a store of lager in his shed -
to tell the truth, he often drank himself stone-dead.
He liked his liquor, was a reg'lar soak,
had been for years, a very boozy moke.
He lacked much company out on the range,
and there had learned to speak. It's nothing strange.
For lonely folk quite often speak alone;
most sensible when all is said and done.
The burro handed him a can of beer.
"'Twas I," he said, and gave a mulish leer.
"Don't be surprised. There's many an ass will squeak
when no one is about to hear it speak.
Now tell me, sir, what brings you to this part?
For by your city dress you' re much too smart
to be a rancher or a wrangler here.
Oh, you've drunk up! Please have another beer."
He passed a second can, and like the first
it slipped down quick. The inspector had a thirst.
He'd had a shock, too, meeting with a moke,
a couth one; very chummy when he spoke.
In brief, they talked of much a good long hour;
by then the inspector's legs had lost their power,
and he was picked up later driving drunk.
The sheriff slapped him in the cooler - clunk!
They laughed him out of court when he explained -
his voice, just like his manner, somewhat strained -
that he'd been sent to find if it were true
that cowboys on the range don't use a loo;
but chapless bend to nature in the raw

when nature prompted them. Against the law,
he said, it was to do that in the wild;
they had to use a loo, leave nature undefiled.
He said the donkey had confirmed the rumor sure,
even though it left him feeling sore.
"That donkey," said the sheriff with a wink,
"will say anything to anyone in drink.
The cowboys here are brung up good an' proper.
That lyin' crittur told you one great whopper!
It don't do a-pryin' into other folks' affairs,
an' catchin' them performin' unawares.
You drove drunk and that you couldn't hide.
I'm giving you, my friend, a week inside."

Nothing he said about his week in jail
when he returned to Washington quite pale.
No one believed a word when he got back,
about a talking donkey off the beaten track.
In truth, the inspector ne'er went West again.
It's said: "When asses speak - beware!" Amen.

SAMSON WEDGE'S PA.

Phoenix town is the driest of dry,
where wit and the desert are one;
but driest of all are the pledgers down there,
the driest folk under the sun.

In Phoenix there lived an abstemious man,
a pledger called Samson Wedge;
teetotaller true if ever there was,
after he'd taken the pledge

way back in the tender years of his youth,
sworn in by his momma, I think,
her pa was a preacher who travelled the west,
on the deadly evils of drink.

He'd lived to a ripe old ninety seven
and his daughter to ninety eight;
but Samson had beaten his mom and her pa,
and they gathered to celebrate

his century, toasting in coffee or tea,
every pledger from far and near;
no liquor had ever once passed their lips,
not a single drop of good cheer.

Samson was solemn as Solomon's seat,
where the king dispensed judgement, they say,
on how to split heirs when mothers fell out
and argued on babies all day.

He was serious as serious on topics of drink,
and declaimed against all types of booze;
saying he owed his health and great age
to tea and an afternoon snooze.

Now Samson never mentioned his pa,
and his friends had assumed he'd passed on;
for his momma and grandpa had lived such long lives
that old Wedgie, they thought, had long gone.

The truth was he'd disappeared searching for gold
high up the Apache Trail;
but he'd gone and got lost in the canyons up there
the day they released him from jail.

Way back, Wedgie senior had been a bad lad,
for he'd held up a steam train or two;
and busted a bank somewhere up north
at a place they call Kalamazoo.

He'd gone off prospecting for gold up the Trail
in the mountains and left them in doubt,
until...you must wait to the end of this tale
to discover how Wedgie made out.

His son made a pile in the grocery trade,
declaring he'd live long and free
from the evil of drink, the Devil's own brew,
so he supped only coffee and tea.

Through the state he was held as a paragon of good,
that you lived to old age in the pink,
if you drank only water or coffee or tea
and stayed all your life clear of drink.

So that when Samson Wedge saw his hundredth year in
they decided to throw a great party;
and they came in their hordes to Samson's fine home,
where he sat holding court hale and hearty.

They baked him a cake and he made a fine speech,
and they cheered and they cheered in accord;
declaring they'd all take the pledge once again
his marvellous feat to record.

When suddenly down from the ceiling above
there came an almighty bump;
then a yell and whoop and a stamping of feet
before another great thump.

The pledgers looked up with fearful eyes,
then all of them did a quick bunk,
when Samson declared very mortified,
"It's my pa! He found gold an' got drunk!"

THE TOMBSTONE PREACHER

Old Wesley McWhinney was known far and wide
throughout Arizona, the state where he died;
preaching the good news right to the end,
pleading with Tombstone to change and amend.

For men down at Tombstone liked women and whisky;
they liked playing cards and sometimes got frisky,
made air so polluted with fast-flying lead,
one whiff of it caught you and left you for dead.

But Preacher McWhinney died peaceful and whole,
and away to the Pearly Gates winged up his soul;
all frilly and white in new robes, no one better,
and as he had promised he sent back a letter.

He let them all know just how well he had done
up there out in space on his heavenly run.
He said he'd arrived at the Gates all askew,
for he'd dropped down stone-dead, plunk in his pew.

His wings and his halo both felt kinda strange,
they'd issued him with at the first interchange;
halfway between earth and heaven on high,
where ready-made outfits are dealt in sky.

Sandals and robes and haloes and harps,
that play divine music in soft flats and sharps;
issued to angels with new sets of wings
to go with the music they play on their strings.

So Wesley arrived at the Gates all brand-new,
and adjusting his halo he joined the short queue
composed of two cowboys from Kansas that day,
who'd picked up some lead when they'd gone to buy hay.

They'd gone to heaven, but their friends down below
had gone where they're grilled in hot ovens set "slow";
the two guys in front had died just before
Preacher McWhinney and stood at the door.

They waited for Peter to open it up
for he'd gone to a snack- bar for something to sup;
he's reg'lar that way and often takes breaks
for it gets very lonely keeping the Gates.

Few folks pass by where he sits for ever,
oiling his locks or doing whatever
needs doing to keep Pearly Gates gleaming,
polishing portals or endlessly dreaming.

He has to check angels who start flying in,
to make sure their slates are quite clean of sin;
the truth is, St Peter has not much to do,
his hours are many, but customers few.

For years sometimes no one goes there at all,
and time then hangs heavy for Peter and Paul
who occasionally drops by to help his pal out,
swapping tall fishermen's tales about trout.

The day Wes McWhinney turned up at his door
and the two in the line had gone in before,
St Peter looked up saying firmly and clear,
"Unless you're checked out, you can't come in here!"

He examined the halo and Wesley's white clothes
over the specs at the end of his nose;
then checked out his sandals and feathers so trim,
to make sure he looked smart before he went in.

For they're very partic'lar in heaven on dress,
and insist you look neat when you stand up to bless,
or sit down on feast-days to heavenly manna,
listening to harps and the odd loud hosanna.

Wesley passed muster all right with his halo,
but then had to tell about all his past lay-low,
the shadier sides of his old earthly life,
when sins and wrong-doings once had been rife.

He admitted to Peter he'd stolen a dollar
or two from the church-plate leaving it hollow,
way back in youth in the church where he prayed;
but Wesley insisted he'd doubly repaid

Every cent he had stolen, the following Sunday.
"I put in my winnings I won at a fun-day,
gambling at Mac's at a card-game deadbeat,
where I have to confess I once tried to cheat."

He admitted he'd drunk hard, paid visits he said
to Big Bertha's roll-about bawdy-house bed;
but that was way back in his rollicking youth,
before he'd reformed and become somewhat couth.

"Any more sins?" Peter asked, very keen.
"You can't enter here unless you come clean."
Wesley thought hard and said very low,
"The last time I sinned was a long time ago.

I've tried to go straight since I turned a new leaf."
But Peter winked back and asked with relief,
"Where do you come from? We must get that clear."
Wesley said proud, "I left Tombstone for here."

"Tombstone?" said Peter. "You're pulling my wing!
You're not trying to fool me just to get in?"
"Indeed not," said Wesley, who looked worried now.
"If you've got a map near, I'll show you I vow."

So Peter pulled out a decrepit old chart,
that Noah had once used navigating the Ark.
They looked and they looked but could find not a glimmer
of Tombstone; and things looked decidedly grimmer

for Wesley to enter the Heavenly City;
St Peter himself began to feel pity,
till Wesley suggested the map was an old one,
and ventured to say that the town was a bold one.

"I'll bet you a buck, if you care to go down, sir,
that you'll find it, St Peter, a mighty fine town, sir."
"Well go back together to your home location,"
said Peter, "the next time I take a vacation.

It's dull around here. I don't have much fun,
and you once led a mighty wild life there, my son."
The saint opened up looking bright as a moonstone,
saying: "Welcome, Saint Wes. You're the first here from
                                        Tombstone!"

THE GLOBE GRAVE-DIGGER

In Globe once lived a man called Enoch Caves,
renowned for digging all the township's graves.
He'd filled folks in round Globe for many a year,
and welcomed them inside from far and near.
Right glad he was to seed his little patch
with coffins sliding down each earthy hatch.
When mourners started up their keening wail,
as Jack the carpenter began to nail
the coffin lid securely down and tight,
then Enoch grew unusually bright.
No happier man despite his dead-end job,
though with the rest he'd wail and weep and sob.
Yet when they'd gone he'd raise a glass on high
to toast the dead. He was a thoughtful guy.
Every day he'd whistle and he'd sing
tra-la, ri-la, and ting-a-ling,
working in the graveyard all alone,
sometimes digging up a skull or bone.
Then he'd chat, like Hamlet, so he said,
with long-gone neighbours once he knew, now dead.
Yet none replied, they were too grave a lot,
too self-contained to put him on the spot.
They'd lost their tongues, you see. Not one could speak.
In Globe no ghost was ever heard to squeak.
Not even after nightfall; never by day,
when ghouls and ghosties have to stay
confined and cribbed in coffins underground,
locked up tight till sunset comes around.
Then they surface, those of them who dare,
to wander forth and take the cool night air.
Or so it's said, though many don't believe it,
and Caves for one would ne'er concede it.
For after dark he'd often wander home

past open graves where ghosts are said to roam.
But experts say you must have psychic powers
to chat with ghosties after opening hours;
when coffins creak and graves yield up their dead,
until the cock crows, then they go to bed.
Not psychic, Caves had never seen a ghost.
Indeed, he'd always made it his proud boast,
that ghosts and spirits never did exist;
all folks had seen were bits of mist.
But one guy in the bar-room where he drank
swore he'd seen a ghost and heard it clank
its chains - and he was most well bred.
The bar-man also saw one hold its head
to speak with him when he'd been on the whisky,
and afterwards the ghost turned kinda frisky,
and started rattling its deadly bones,
walking round the house with fiendish moans,
haunting him throughout the night in bed.
Since then he'd never touched a drop, he said.
But Enoch glibly scorned each ghostly tale,
until the night he hit the homeward trail,
which took him past the deepest grave he'd made.
Full fifteen feet he'd delved that day with spade.
The new hole gaped awaiting its first guest
boxed neat and tidy for th' eternal rest;
secure and silent, out of sight of all,
until that final golden trumpet-call.
Alas, a guest called Sid was in already,
a hobo very drunk and most unsteady,
he'd blundered in an hour or so before,
and landed at the bottom feeling sore.
The night was dark, as black as black could be,
and so the hobo moved round warily.
He tried to scale the walls with all his might,

but then packed up and settled for the night,
pulling his coat around him to keep warm,
and curling up to sleep until the dawn.
An hour went by and Enoch came along,
full to the brim and singing a merry song.
He also went adrift and made the drop,
plunk into the grave, just like the hobo - plop!
Sidney woke up as Enoch hit the deck,
fumbling around and grumbling like heck;
as Sid sat still as stone and stayed there dumb,
feeling grim and looking mighty glum.
But in the end he felt he had to speak,
and whispered quiet, his voice all thin and weak,
"You'll not get outa here, old friend," said Sid.
But he was wrong - for Enoch did!
And now when ghostly tales are getting steep,
he tells of how he made that mighty leap.

THE GLOBE GRAVE DIGGER SEQUEL

"Revenge," the adage runs, "is always sweet."
Not true! Experience tells it's much more sweet,
and safer still, to turn the other cheek.
The Good Book, too, declares it is the meek
who one day shall inherit all the earth.
And earth is very much the theme of mirth
which prompted this true tale; leastways a hole
from which the earth had been removed, dug
carefully and deep by one as smug
as Billy Smiley's cat which caught a mouse
and took it home. It thought it owned the house,
but soon learned otherwise when old Ma Smiley
saw it dead. She didn't think too highly
of it in her bed and hollared loud,
near fit to raise two cadavers in shroud.
For Billy Smiley was Globe town's mortician.
He'd stored next-door two stiffs in good condition,
inside his morgue behind the entrance porch,
waiting for their last ride to the church,
at peace and quiet. Well, like I said,
when Billy's missus yelled to raise the dead,
those two guys stirred - but settled down again
to wait their final ride, true gentlemen.
No reneging when certified as dead,
they took their death-certificates as read,
signed by Doctor Leech, new to the town.
It wouldn't have been quite right to put him down,
him newly qualified and all. Sure blown
his reputation if they'd flown
the morgue and made the doctor look a fool;
Smiley, too, who'd got them up real cool,
best they'd ever looked for years on ice.
But to my tale - and it's a tale right grave

of how revenge back-fired on Enoch Caves,
who, you remember, had a nasty fright
and leapt a goodly fifteen feet one night;
the night a hobo scared him from his wits -
well and truly gave smug Caves the shits.
For hard-nosed Caves had always bragged the boast
he didn't believe his graveyard had a ghost.
He made himself look stupid, good and proper,
when he gasped his conversation-stopper
in the bar, which he'd just left to walk
across the graveyard to his home; stalk
the stormy night as black as coffin pitch.
Pride comes before a fall. He didn't know what from
                                         which

when he dropped plunk into an open grave,
dug by himself that very day. Caves
fell in drunk and dropped the fifteen feet.
Unseen and at the bottom, set to greet
him sat a hobo, who'd dropped in an hour
or two before. He'd settled down to wait
first light. He, too, had tippled rather late.
Enoch made that mighty famous leap
when the hobo spoke and said the steep
sides would that night entomb them both.
The sexton with a vitriolic oath
took off, leapt fifteen formidable feet
and hared it to the crowded bar-room neat,
babbling that he'd heard a ghostie speak.
Out rushed the entire bar to take a peek
inside the grave. Caves never lived it down.
He was the laughing-stock of town,
and swore he'd get revenge upon the guy
who'd made him jump so squarely at the sky -
that hobo, when he next arrived in town,

and wandered through the graveyard to kip down
inside the shed where Enoch kept his tools:
his spade, his mattock, barrow and the stool
he sat upon when resting from his toil;
labouring in the graveyard, piling up the spoil
beside each grave he dug. He was a master
sexton, no one better digging faster.
Globe had a priceless gem in Enoch Caves,
the finest architect of new-dug graves,
who had for years stacked Globites prim and neat
to sleep their final sleep. Quite a feat,
to tell the truth, the ground made digging grim -
though easy work when filling them all in,
as Enoch Caves was soon to find that day,
fired with revenge to give that guy his pay,
his come-uppance for the howling shame
he'd brought on Caves. Sidney was his name.
A tidy guy, they said, who hailed from Tombstone,
hoping to find gold in Globe, his moonstone.
But he never did. Struck it rich
another way. He made the double-switch
at cards when they were drunk and gambling mad.
Took Globe one night for every buck it had -
but that's another tale. One dismal night
Enoch waited for the hobo right
at the bottom of a newly open grave.
The sky was black, the moon a watery shroud,
fitful gleaming through the scudding cloud
as Sidney strolled unwittingly to bed,
the funeral bier that stood in Enoch's shed.
And as he passed the open grave he heard
the weirdest wailing. His hair stirred.
His blood froze. But only momentarily.
He recognised the voice, peeped in to see

the sexton who'd called so eerily below.
He was about to say to him: "Hello!"
when vengeful Enoch wailed on high again:
"It sure is cold down here, I tell you plain!"
Sidney smiled a quiet smile; picked
up a handy spade and shovelled quick
a spade or two of spoil piled up around,
then shouted down that black hole in the ground:
"Of course you're cold. You ain't filled in, old friend.
You'll warm up fast with earth on top. I'll send
more spadefuls down. Just say the word!"
I can't repeat to you what Sidney heard,
but he let down the graveyard ladder,
and out came Enoch, wiser far but sadder;
begged the man from Tombstone seal his lips,
which he did. Kept 'em tight as zips.
Old Enoch lost all vengeance, grew more grave;
filled in, he'd learned his lesson and forgave.

MOMMA DENCH'S EGG-TIMER

Old Momma Dench was the hardest wench this side of the
North Fork Pass,
and in heaven's name I pity the dame who's harder than
that old lass.
For she had a stare that'd scoot a bear or stampede a
moose with fright,
and her voice was as gruff as a road that's rough when the
grader's scraping it right.

She panned for gold in the coldest cold by melting the
mud with her breath,
in weather so wild men wept like a child at the cold that
near froze 'em to death.
She fished snug and nice through a hole in the ice till her
huskies howled themselves dumb;
then she cussed 'em quiet to stop the riot they made from
the frost in their bum.

She was iron-hard because of a pard she'd married way
back in youth,
when her face was sweet and her figure neat - and her
manners not so uncouth.
For I'm glad to opine, once on a time, Ma Dench was the
purtiest gal,
and many's the guy who's cried his heart dry when she
stood him up for his pal.

But sad to relate she chose for her mate the laziest guy in
town;
though he looked a swell, he was idle as hell when its fires
have burned clean down.
Dan Dench was his name, and in Yukon his fame spread
afar for his idle life,
yet he wasn't so crazy to stop being lazy after he made her
his wife.

He did not a stroke that lazy-bone soak from the moment
                                he made her his bride,
for he'd rise about noon and hit the saloon till the barman
                                bounced him outside.
Then he'd hang around town with his hands dug deep
                        down in his pockets to keep 'em warm,
doing nothing all day the easy way till he went home to
                                face the storm.

Momma's language was hot, but Dan cared not a jot, just
                                going his idle ways,
and the harder she worked, the more Danny shirked, right
                                to the end of his days.
For Danny dropped dead from boredom it's said, too lazy
                                to move to the shade,
one hot day in June, not long after noon, dried out and
                                rod-stiff as a spade.

Friends came far and near to shed their last tear, and to
                                sorrow and sympathise
with old Widow Dench, who sat dumb on a bench saying
                                nothing of Danny's demise.
Some started to cry, and some looked at the sky and said
                                that they'd pray were there need;
but most folks that day, I'm sorry to say, had come for a
                                beer and a feed.

And strangest of all was no coffin or pall, just the widow
                                sat still as a stave;
and the mourners sure itched to know how she'd fixed to
                                have Danny put by with no grave.
"I had him burned slow, just three days ago, in the boiler
                                behind the saloon,"
she explained as they gasped, and they saw that she
                                clasped a glass tube like a little balloon.

Then she held it on high for all there to spy, as she turned
                                                    it around and around,
a timer for eggs that you put on a ledge to make sure that
                                            they're done firm and sound.
"I didn't have no urn, for there weren't much to burn of
                                        old Danny, he dried up so fast,"
she cried out aloud, as she showed to the crowd her
                                        egg-timer filled with his ash.

She held it up high and sighed a sweet sigh watching her
                                            spouse trickle through,
then her voice grew quite soft when she held it aloft, and
                                        her smile became much softer, too.
She beamed with sheer bliss as she planted a kiss on the
                                        timer along with this vow:
"He never worked hard in his life, my old pard - but by
                                    crikee he's gonna work now!"

THE DUDE COUNSELLOR

Sir Reginald Goode was the doodiest dude
this side of the Great Divide;
from head to toe the dandiest beau
he took every gal in his stride.

They swooned in flocks o'er his well-combed locks
and his dark eyes fathoms deep;
he'd only to smile and they'd ride a mile,
just to get another peep

of those flashing teeth lying underneath
his wild lips oozing passion;
which had kissed the best right across the West,
every dame in the height of fashion.

He was sterling bred, from England they said,
and he spoke like a Brit sweet and plummy,
in accents so smooth he could gun-slingers soothe,
and leave them all pally and chummy.

He'd fled to the States driven there by the Fates,
for he'd blotted his book back at home,
where his dad was a duke, who'd given him the spook,
and he'd had to bolt over the foam.

All because of a gal, whose name was Sal,
a countess who gave him her heart;
and much else, it's said, once they'd jumped into bed,
where Sir Reg played a most manly part.

He sure had his fling, but had had to take wing,
nine months later when called to account
by his blue-bloodied dad, who called him a cad;
and so did Sal's husband, the count.

In the States he made pards he beat hollow at cards,
and licked 'em at gun-slinging, too,
when they called him a cheat; for he drew fast and neat
to drill them with holes through and through.

He'd become somewhat smoother by the time he reached
Yuma,
and quietened down greatly at Why;
When he checked in at Tucson, he'd stopped being a loose
'un
and befriended a really nice guy.

He was called Billy Nooks who sold all the books
in the town at his store near the bar;
he was small with a stammer and lacked any glamour,
with dames he didn't get far.

Though he loved all the gals like the rest of his pals,
he hadn't a clue how to draw
one sweet little pet into his net,
from the beauties who came to his store.

They bought purple novels which gave 'em the wobbles,
and set them off sighing all night;
when they'd dream of Sir Goode and the way that he
stood,
strong and firm, oh, so manly, upright.

From the first flush of youth, Sir Reg had been couth,
and read well-written books by the score;
so he made quite a friend of young Billy, who'd lend
him the best of his stock in his store.

Bill envied Sir Reg with all his fine edge,
which could pull the gals easy as pie;
so one day Billy Nooks, as Reg browsed through his
                                                    books,
asked the dude how to catch a girl's eye.

"Dear Billy, old chappie, you must make her happy.
It's easy once you've learned the trick.
You tattle and tittle, not much nor too little,
and practise the smooth-talk so slick.

Then give her a treat, not too dry nor too sweet,
of the best wine they've got in the bar;
You buy her a meal, an' **that's** when you feel
your way into her heart from afar."

"An' then?" queried Billy, trying not to look silly.
"And then you light candles of love,"
replied Reggie the dude, who all the while chewed
sweet liquorice and spoke like a dove.

"And while you're sat eating, you must keep repeating
the love-music she likes to hear;
on your Spanish guitar, the soft dolce-dah,
not too distant, nor yet over-near."

"An' then?" whispered Billy, as white as a lily,
drinking in Reggie's advice.
"Just keep up the love-words - before moving bedwards,
not fast nor too slow, but real nice."

"Go on!" gulped young Nooks, Tucson's seller of books,
"What must I do then?" was his plea.
"Why then, my dear Billy, as she lies pink and frilly,
why then you rush back and get me!"

THE SUSPENDED PREACHER
There was a man styled Brother Larry Leake,
who had a TV program twice a week;
on which they beamed his smiling face afar
through every network by a satellite star.
He was a handsome guy, well trimmed and oiled;
his hands were manicured and never soiled.
You see, he had an allergy to work,
a tendency all honest toil to shirk;
for Brother Leake learned early on in youth,
his earnest face and tongue were certain proof
against all work involving sweat of brow;
some deeper cunning instinct told him how
to make his fortune a much easier way;
and thus he turned to preaching for his pay.
His homilies were airy froth and foam,
their theme was: 'Charity begins at home.'
And as you'll see the homes he owned were swell;
the television chat-show paid him well.
His words were windy as the boundless sea
whenever he had cause to speak on charity.
Sadly, he never practised what he'd preach;
integrity was far beyond his reach.
The depths of bland hypocrisy he'd plumb
and speak for hours on faith, till kingdom come.
And as he preached he'd tune his golden tongue
to make the money ring; and soon he'd wrung
the audience, his willing listeners bone-dry.
In truth, he didn't really have to try.
In time his hair turned grey, then silvery white;
combed smooth each day to make it shiny bright
and make him look the perfect holy saint -
and make the money flow without constraint.
He bought a city penthouse. Soon he'd four,

and mansions up the West Coast by the score.
Each had its golf course and its swimming pools,
all paid for by his flock, the silly fools!
That selfsame flock, oh, how he knew to please 'em;
how he sharpened up his shears to fleece 'em.
He'd ask a million bucks a month - and got it.
Not to the Lord it went, but his own pocket.
He never married. He'd no need of that;
for many a lady friend dropped in to chat.
He owned a string of horses, hired two grooms,
two well blessed wenches, gave them penthouse rooms
rent-free and furnished by dear Brother Leake,
who paid them pastoral visits every week.
They polished up his tackle neat and trim.
Riding, so he said, was good for him.
It kept him in the pink his daily trot,
ready for his television slot.
As backing he acquired an angel band,
clean-cut songsters always at his hand;
drilled to perfection in expensive dress,
coming in on cue when he began to bless
inside his glitzy church, the very best.
"A sanctuary where everyone finds rest,"
was blazed in foot-high letters on the portal;
and Larry Leake, I fear, began to feel immortal.
Yet pride we all know comes before a fall,
and Brother Larry one day shocked them all
by plunging unexpectedly from grace,
suspended by his trousers out in space.
That day he'd climbed up to the highest spire
of his church, he couldn't get any higher,
to preach to those beneath. Oh, what a sight
he had that day from such a dizzy height!
And with what force the bogus fellow preached.

Alas, self-righteous man, he over-reached
himself and stumbled on the narrow ledge,
and in an instant dropped clean off the edge,
and would have well and truly been forsaken
had not a friendly flagstaff saved his bacon.
By chance, his trousers caught the flagpole strut,
which left him hanging mid-air by the butt;
eyes wide with horror, staring at the ground,
his tongue cleft to his palate, not a sound
that noisy instrument could make or utter;
but finally he managed one weak stutter,
lifting up his frightened gaze on high:
"Is anybody there? Lord, help me or I die!"
To his surprise he heard a voice above:
"Let go, my son! I'll bear you up with love."
Leake glanced below, then croaked another prayer:
"Dear Lord, is anybody else up there?"
The heavens were silent. Leake was left suspended,
hung by his butt, undignified, upended;
begging forgiveness for his past, repentant,
his life entirely on his pants dependent.
So, in suspense an hour the poor guy prayed,
until the good Lord sent the fire-brigade,
who brought the preacher safely down their ladder,
a wiser man, if weaker in the bladder.
From that day forth he never preached again,
gave all his wealth away and lived quite plain;
piously declaring how it came to pass
he'd seen the light suspended by his bottom.

THE HEN-PECKED RANCHER
There was a dame called Edna Gort,
her tongue was long, her husband short;
they ran a ranch for many a day,
somewhere up Montana way.
Now, Tommy Gort though short in limb
was big in frame and pretty trim;
he boxed, he wrestled, rodeod,
at odd times, too, he romeod.
But that was in his younger days;
when be got wed he changed his ways,
for Edna watched him like a hawk -
and jeepers! how that dame could talk.
She'd talk the hind leg off a hound.
Non-stop she went; for round and round,
and in and out, her tongue, it seems,
continued talking in her dreams.
For when she'd gone to bed and slept,
she kept on telling how she kept
the ranch and home and all therein
gleaming like a brand-new pin.
And rashly once Tom tried to stop her,
but got his ears clipped good and proper.
He'd barely said: "If I'd my way..."
when she cut in and had her say.
Rattling her tongue round in her head,
she dinned the poor guy almost dead.
"If you'd your way you'd bring disgrace!
I'd never dare to show my face.
Could you but change with me a week,
you'd never have the nerve to speak
of what you'd do if you had your way.
Be thankful, Gort, content to stay
just as you are in your present state,

47

carried around by me on a plate.
I cook and wash and iron each week,
with never a word, so quiet and meek;
while you ride out with the boys to town,
turning the whole place upside down;
drinking and gambling the whole day long,
so drunk you scarce know right from wrong;
and I slave here till you come back again.
You don't know you're born at times, you men!"
"I'd only like to say..." said Tom,
but Edna blew up in his face like a bomb.
"You always say too much, Tom Gort.
Just hold your tongue! Weren't you ever taught
'An open mouth holds nothing but air'?
Have you nothing to do but stand and stare,
keeping me here with your idle chatter,
stopping me doing the things that matter?
Tom shot off and left her talking,
near-deafened by her raucous squawking;
for Edna's tongue was like a Tartar,
it made Tom Gort a living martyr,
a reg'lar saint through life unsung,
tormented by her fiery tongue.
And at the end as death drew nigh,
and Tom was heading for the sky,
the preacher came to say a prayer
at Tommy's bedside on a chair.
The other side was Tommy's wife;
the first time in their married life
silent as a muffled bell,
waiting to toll the funeral knell.
The preacher prayed and Tommy sighed,
Edna dabbed her eyes and cried,
watching Tom slip down the bed,

so short they only saw his head,
a tuft of hair upon his crown
the rest of him had gone right down.
When suddenly he lay quite still,
no sound at all and Tom grew chill.
The preacher felt his pulse and said:
"Mrs Gort, your husband's dead."
But, no, from underneath the sheet
a voice protested faint but fleet:
"I'm still alive! I haven't gone!"
Old Edna glared and thereupon
lashed Tommy Gort with all her might:
"Just hold your tongue! The *preacher's* right!"
So Tom sent forth a final sigh,
then quietly winged his way on high.

THE SENATOR'S FALSE TEETH

All politicians use the same foul pot;
they're all alike, an empty loud-mouthed lot.
Party or creed, it doesn't matter which,
they're painted with a similar brand of pitch.
Like lawyers they will argue black is white;
swear right is wrong; more often wrong is right.
And such a one was Senator Elmer Louth,
famed right across the States for his big mouth.
I do declare there never was a match
to vie with Elmer Louth's wide-open hatch.
I'm told it never closed by day or night;
and opened wide it was a ghastly sight,
full of teeth and full of garbage wind
stored in an empty vessel thickest-skinned.
Harsh word or insult not a jot he heeded;
advice, of course, he never felt was needed.
Upon the stage at every state convention
his promises were masterly invention.
Election pledges, every cherished tenet
evaporated once he reached the Senate.
For politicians' promises are random;
easy made, they're shed with wild abandon,
dropped like leaves at fall before the wind.
That they promise most, they most rescind.
Now, once when Elmer Louth was at a rally -
leading his listeners down some blind alley,
selling them short with tricksy tedious tale,
in which his windy promises flew thick as hail;
pledging this and fiercely pledging that,
talking trough his politician's hat -
he opened up his mouth for once too wide,
when he'd gotten smoothly in his stride.
For suddenly there came an awful splatter,

and then a terrible splint'ring clatter,
as out his false teeth shot like podded beans
and smashed upon the floor in smithereens.
The Senator stood dumbfounded and aghast;
his barn-door mouth at once shut tight and fast,
his hand clamped tight across the cavernous gape,
which left him looking foolish as an ape;
pondering how he'd finish off his speech
untoothed, with no spare dentures within reach.
His cause seemed lost and Elmer Louth was fraught;
but to his aid an honest guy, he thought,
rose slowly from the audience beneath,
to offer him a brand-new set of teeth.
If they would play for time and serve the drink,
he'd find new teeth for Elmer in a twink.
Indeed, unlike the Senator, he kept his word,
was back before they knew he'd even stirred.
He parked outside a long black limousine
where many sets of dentures could be seen.
Row on row of false teeth, top and bottom,
all large size and gleaming. How he got 'em
can't be told, but everyone agreed
he came on cue in Elmer's hour of need;
and one by one he tried them in his hatch,
until at last he had the perfect match,
and opened up his mouth - though not so wide -
revealing the new dentures sat inside.
The helpful stranger said his name was Jones;
he spoke in hushed and kinda sombre tones.
Dressed in black most dignified and neat.
from top to toe, from sober face to feet.
He said he had to leave to do some work,
some urgent business which he couldn't shirk.
So, next day Elmer went to pay his debt

and thank the quiet stranger for the set
of teeth he'd brought to help him end his speech,
assuming he'd a dentistry in reach.
But no, he worked the other side of town,
a place that few folk cared to wander round,
and when they did, they didn't need new dentures;
those treated there were set on other ventures.
Elmer found the place and read the sign,
and as he read a chill ran down his spine.
No mention there of dentist or physician,
just: *"Jerry Jones, Embalmer and Mortician."*
He left the teeth behind, his need was met,
and ever after carried a spare set.

THE TESLIN TEA-PARTY

Matilda O'Gilly from Teslin gave a meal at her house one
                                                        fine day;
it was a most solemn occasion, very reverent too in its
                                                        way.
The dean and his wife drove from Whitehorse, for the
                                        bishop had gone for a swim,
in the hot-springs to think out his sermon and keep in
                                                episcopal trim.

The reason they gathered together was a sad one, I'm
sorry   to say.
to give their respects to her husband, their final devotions
                                                        to pay.
For Billy had gone in a car-crash, when he'd argued
                                        head-on with a truck,
full-loaded with ore on the highway and speeding from
                                                Faro, worse luck.

Poor Billy had been born in England, at a place that's
                                        called Yorkshire back there,
renowned through the world for its puddings, as light and
                                                as crisp as fresh air.
Young Billy had come full of promise to the Yukon for
                                                fortune and fame,
and he'd worked hard to build up a business, succeeding
                                                in making a name.

For years he'd intended to go back, to Yorkshire that's
                                                famous for weft,
but fate and his fortune forestalled him, and he never
                                                returned once he left.
Now he drove a fast car up in Yukon, where everyone
goes   on the right,
not left as they do back in England, where roads are all
                                                wiggly and tight.
He thought he'd best get in some practice, on the highway

53

that went past his door,
the highway that goes to Alaska, with coaches and trucks
by the score.
Nothing drove by when he stared, one still summer's day
about noon,
and soon he was clocking up ninety down the *left* of the
highway, the loon!

The trucker had no chance to miss him. They heard up at
Skagway the crash,
when Billy O'Gilly from Teslin was turned into motorway
hash.
His widow she had all cremated they managed to scrape
from the deck,
and put in teapot for safety, an antique she'd bought upon
spec.

She hid him away for safe-keeping in the kitchen up high,
out of reach,
until she had time to inter him at his favourite spot on the
beach.
So sat in his teapot serenely he awaited his last
resting-place,
while everyone gathered for dinner and the dean bowed his
head to say grace.

Then suddenly out of the kitchen there came a peculiar
wail,
the kettle had stared to whistle like an engine hot-rodding
the rail.
The dean's wife rushed out from the parlour; the kettle was
snatched from the fire.
to stop it distracting the others, whose minds were on
matters much higher.

And while they were at their devotions, the dean's wife
began to look round,

to try and locate Tilly's teapot before they all came back to
ground.
Her eye fell upon Billy's tea-urn and without more ado on
the spot,
she plonked in ten teaspoons on Billy, on top of his ash in
the pot!

Poor Billy felt mightily dropped on, but had to sit still and
keep mum,
as hot water was poured on his ashes - and Tilly his wife
was struck dumb.
She was quite lost for words as they swallowed, could not
think at all what so say,
as cupful by cupful her husband was poured out at teatime
that day.

As they drew near the end of the party, she felt she must
speak out or burst,
for she'd heard them pass comments quite clearly that the
tea had a kind of burnt taste.
"It's Billy," she yelled, "you've been drinking!" and
explained where she'd hidden her spouse;
the company looked ashen and queasy - and some of them
fled from the house.

They returned in a while more comported and the dean
saved the day like a friend,
by proposing to give the committal as well as a blessing to
end.
He entrusted their brother departed to God's gracious
keeping above,
committing dear Billy to nature since they'd drunk him all
up with their love.

A TALE FROM THE WEST RIDING

When I was young and the sap ran high
as wayward as the moon;
the town and valley throbbed with life
which glowed like the sun at noon;
then time stretched out a winding lane,
un-ending, out of sight;
where youth and time went on and on,
like stars on cloudless night.

But now that I'm old and dry as a stick,
and plod like my doggerel rhyme,
the town and the valley are changed, quite changed,
transformed with me by time;
for only crumbling shells remain,
dead as my manhood's rut;
and ghosts slink through the familiar ways
where others now swagger and strut.